Grade

4

Name

Date of exam

Contents

Editor for ABRSM: Richard Jones

Other pieces for this grade

† This arrangement only

First published in 2010 by ABRSM (Publishing) Ltd, a wholly owned subsidiary of ABRSM, 24 Portland Place, London W1B 1LU, United Kingdom

© 2010 by The Associated Board of the Royal Schools of Music

Music origination by Barnes Music Engraving Ltd
Cover by Økvik Design
Printed in England by Caligraving Ltd, Thetford, Norfolk

A:1

Allegro in F

No. 33 from *Nannerl Notenbuch*

Anon.

Nannerl Notenbuch Notebook for Nannerl

This piece comes from a collection that Leopold Mozart (1719–87) compiled in 1759 for his eight-year-old daughter Maria Anna, nicknamed Nannerl (sister of Wolfgang Amadeus), whom he was teaching to play the piano at that time. Quavers might be lightly detached throughout. Dynamics are editorial suggestions only.

Source: L. Mozart: *Nannerl-Notenbuch*, 1759; original manuscript, property of the Internationale Stiftung Mozarteum, Salzburg

Scherzo

from *Musikalische Nebenstunden*

J. C. F. Bach

Musikalische Nebenstunden Musical Leisure Hours

Johann Christoph Friedrich Bach (1732–95), the second youngest son of Johann Sebastian Bach, entered the service of Count Wilhelm of Schaumburg-Lippe in Bückeburg in 1750. He was promoted to the post of Konzertmeister in 1759 and remained at the court for the rest of his life. He was admired as a keyboard virtuoso as well as a composer. His miscellany *Musikalische Nebenstunden*, from which this scherzo is taken, contains not only keyboard pieces but also cantatas and songs. In the scherzo, most unslurred quavers might be lightly detached. The opening *f* and the one in b. 32 have been added by the editor.

Source: *Musikalische Nebenstunden*, 4 vols. (Rinteln, 1787–8)

Minuet in G

No. 2 from Six Minuets, WoO 10

Ludwig van Beethoven

Fine

In 1792, at the age of 21, Beethoven settled in Vienna, where he was feted by the local aristocracy, establishing himself as a piano virtuoso, at first in private homes, but from 1795 in public too. That year he is thought to have composed the Six Minuets, WoO 10, in their original orchestral version which, however, no longer survives. The Minuet in G comes from Beethoven's own keyboard version, which dates from the following year. The dynamics at the start of each strain of the minuet are editorial suggestions only, as are the slurs in bb. 24 (RH) and 32 (LH) of the trio.
Source: *VI Menuetten für das Clavier* (Vienna: Artaria, 1796)

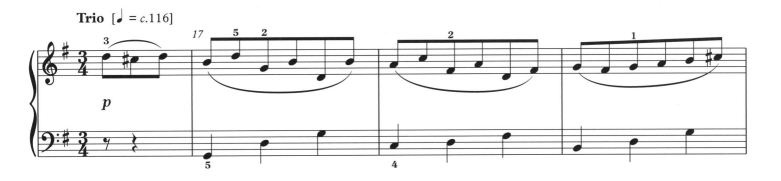

D.C. al Fine

Alone at Sunset

No. 10 from *Sea Idylls*

Walter Carroll

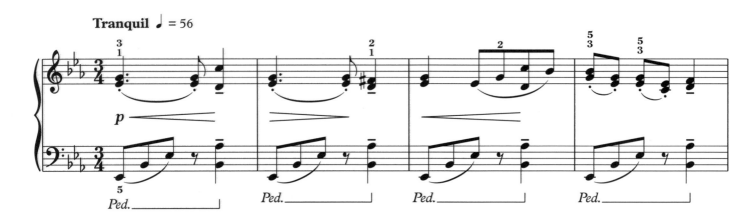

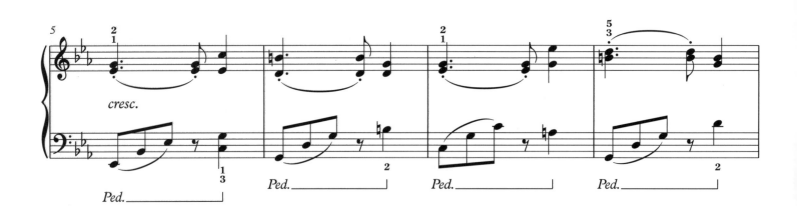

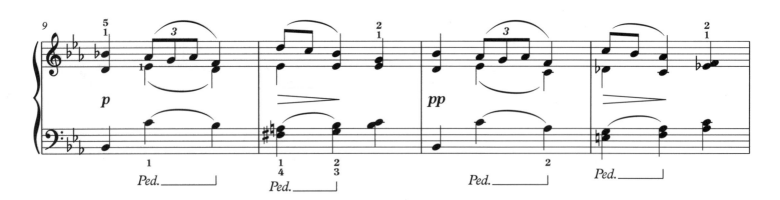

Walter Carroll (1869–1955) was a Manchester-born music educator and composer. He played a vital role in the musical life of his native city, teaching at the Royal Manchester College of Music and at Manchester University, and acting as Music Adviser to the Local Education Authority. He composed many fine elementary piano pieces for children. Of *Sea Idylls* he wrote: 'These little pieces should be regarded as short studies in colouring and expression. They are sound-pictures in miniature, suggested by recollections of a visit to the beautiful rockbound shores of Galloway, where the mystery of the sea and the fire of the sunset weave their magic spell around a coast-line full of romantic interest.' 'Alone at Sunset' is prefaced by a motto from Shelley: '… And there the sea I found / Calm as a cradled child in dreamless slumber bound.' For a more flowing feel, this piece might be played at a slightly faster tempo, e.g. ♩ = 66. Either this tempo or the composer's metronome mark would be acceptable for this piece in the exam. In b. 11, the editor has added a slur in the lower RH part by analogy with b. 9.

Source: *Sea Idylls: Ten Miniatures* (London & Manchester: Forsyth Bros. Ltd, 1914)

B:2

Waltz

No. 23 from *24 Little Pieces*, Op. 39

D. B. Kabalevsky

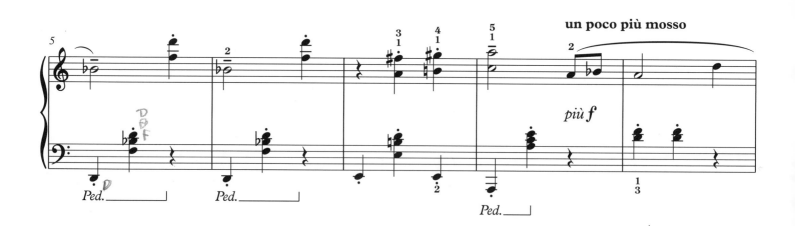

The Russian composer Dmitry Borisovich Kabalevsky (1904–87) studied piano and composition at the Moscow Conservatory, where he later taught, being appointed professor in 1939. He was active in the field of music education and wrote much music for children, such as the *24 Little Pieces*, Op. 39, from which this waltz is taken.

B:3

Chez le forgeron

No. 5 from *Novelettes mignonnes*, Op. 8

Edited by Alan Jones

S. M. Maikapar

Chez le forgeron At the Smithy; **Novelettes mignonnes** Little Novelettes

The Ukrainian composer and pianist Samuil Moiseyevich Maikapar (1867–1938) was a student at the St Petersburg Conservatory, where he was employed as professor of piano from 1910 to 1930. Almost all of his compositions are for the piano – many of them miniatures written for children, notably the collection *Novelettes mignonnes*, Op. 8, which contains this musical picture of a blacksmith's workshop.

Reproduced from *A Romantic Sketchbook for Piano*, Book II, edited by Alan Jones (ABRSM)

Soldiers in the Distance

from *Fantasies*

Arthur Benjamin

Quick-march time [♩ = *c.*116]
As strictly in time as possible from beginning to end

Arthur Benjamin (1893–1960) was an Australian-born composer and pianist who studied composition with Stanford at the Royal College of Music from 1911 to 1914. He taught piano at the Sydney Conservatory from 1919 to 1921, then settled in London, becoming a professor at the Royal College of Music in 1926. His piano pupils included Britten. Of 'Soldiers in the Distance' the composer wrote: 'Tone control is all-important here. Play the staccatos as though the keys were red-hot. Even in the legato marks in the RH the fingers must be clearly articulated. And of course you will not play all the crotchets in the LH alike; make the *tiniest* accent on the strong beats. You will find it necessary to give the tied semibreves enough tone to keep them vibrating through two bars.'
Source: *Fantasies for Piano Solo* (London: Winthrop Rogers, 1933)

C:2

Carnival in Rio

William Gillock

William Gillock (1917–93) was an American music educator and composer of piano music. He lived and worked for many years in New Orleans, then later in the Dallas area. *Carnival in Rio* is a samba, a Brazilian dance that plays a major role in the annual carnival celebrations in Rio de Janeiro, hence the title.

Blues

from *Melody and Rhythm*

Gerard Hengeveld

Gerard Hengeveld (1910–2001) was a Dutch pianist, composer and teacher. He studied piano and composition at the Amsterdam Conservatory from 1924 to 1928 and subsequently appeared for many years as a soloist throughout Europe. He taught piano at the conservatories in The Hague and Amsterdam. As a composer he is best known for his educational piano pieces. In 'Blues', the dotted rhythms should be swung. Editorial rests have been added in bb. 5, 21 and 25 to clarify the part-writing.

© 1961 by Broekmans & Van Poppel B. V., Amsterdam
Used with permission. All enquiries about this piece, apart from those directly relating to the exams, should be addressed to Broekmans & Van Poppel B. V., Van Baerlestraat 92–94, 1071 BB Amsterdam, The Netherlands.